The Sh

DICK KING-SMITH

Level 2

Retold by Chris Grant-Bear
Series Editors: Andy Hopkins and Jocelyn Potter

Pearson Education Limited
Edinburgh Gate, Harlow,
Essex CM20 2JE, England
and Associated Companies throughout the world.

ISBN: 978-1-4058-6974-4

First published by Penguin Books Ltd 1997
Published by Addison Wesley Longman Ltd and Penguin Books Ltd 1998
New edition first published 1999
This edition first published 2008

1 3 5 7 9 10 8 6 4 2

Typeset by Graphicraft Ltd, Hong Kong
Set in 11/14pt Bembo
Printed in China
SWTC/01

Published by Pearson Education Ltd in association with
Penguin Books Ltd, both companies being subsidiaries of Pearson Plc

For a complete list of the titles available in the Penguin Readers series please write to your local
Pearson Longman office or to: Penguin Readers Marketing Department, Pearson Education,
Edinburgh Gate, Harlow, Essex CM20 2JE, England.

Contents

Introduction

'Mum,' said Babe. 'Why can't I learn to be a sheep-pig?'

Who is Babe? And what is a sheep-pig?

The Hoggets have a sheep farm near a village. One day, there is a party in the village, and Farmer Hogget wins a pig! Mrs Hogget is happy because there is a lot of meat on a pig. The pig isn't happy. His name is Babe and he wants his mother.

Farmer Hogget has a very good sheepdog. Her name is Fly. She is kind to Babe and they are quickly friends. But what can a pig do on a sheep farm? A dog works with the sheep, but a pig can't do that . . . or can it?

Babe is a very clever pig. Fly and Farmer Hogget teach Babe, and Babe is better than the sheepdogs! But can he be the best in Britain? He learns to talk to the sheep. Will the sheep help him?

Dick King Smith was born in England in 1922. He was a farmer for twenty years. His farm was in Gloucestershire in the west of England. He loved all his animals and gave them names. He had a pig for many years. The pig's name was Monty.

But farmers must also be good with numbers. 'I'm good with words but not good with numbers,' he says. So he started to teach in the village school. The children enjoyed his stories about his farm, and he started to write books for children and young people. Many of his stories are about farmers and their animals. Two of his famous stories are *The Fox Busters* and *The Hodgeheg*.

Babe, the film of Dick's story, *The Sheep-Pig*, came to cinemas in 1995. Then there was a second film in 1998. They called it *Babe: Pig in the City*.

Chapter 1   Fourteen Kilos of Pig

'What's that noise?' Mrs Hogget asked. She looked out of her kitchen window. 'Listen, can you hear it? What's happening?'

Farmer Hogget listened. Then he looked at his watch and said, 'It's the party down in the village. Starts at two o'clock.'

'I know that,' his wife said. 'But what's that other noise?'

'It's a pig,' said Farmer Hogget.

'A pig!' Mrs Hogget listened again. 'Yes, it's a pig! But who's got pigs in our village? Everybody's got sheep round here, not pigs. Well, well...take this food for the party with you, and have a good time.'

Farmer Hogget drove to the village in his big truck. He went to look for the noisy pig. He found it in a small sheep-pen near the church.

'Morning, Farmer Hogget,' the man with the pig said. 'Do you want this pig? Can you say how heavy he is? Come on! Buy a ticket...it's only ten pence.'

'I'm a sheep farmer...I don't have pigs,' said Farmer Hogget. Then he looked at the little fat pig in the corner of the sheep-pen. Carefully, Farmer Hogget took the little pig in his arms. The pig was very quiet. It made no more noise.

'Well, well, he likes you! Come on, how heavy is he?'

'Fourteen kilos, I think,' he said.

The man wrote '14' in a book next to Farmer Hogget's name and telephone number. Farmer Hogget paid his ten pence and got his ticket. Then he drove home.

Carefully, Farmer Hogget took the little pig in his arms.
The pig was very quiet. It made no more noise.

In the kitchen Mrs Hogget listened to her husband's story.

She smiled. 'There's a lot of meat on a pig...I can make a good dinner or two out of a big, fat pig, you know...Oh, listen now, there's the phone.'

Chapter 2   A New Mum for Babe

Fly was Farmer Hogget's black and white sheepdog.★ She was
the mother of four young dogs. They were going to be sheepdogs, too. Fly looked at them and was happy.

'They're good, clever dogs. Soon they must leave me, but
they're learning their lessons well,' she thought.

'Good boys,' Fly said. 'Stop now. Here's the boss.'

Farmer Hogget drove his truck into the yard. He took a
box out of the back and carried it across the yard into the
stable.

'What's in the box, Mum?' one of the young dogs asked.

'A pig,' Fly said.

'What's the boss going to do with a pig?' another dog asked.

'Eat it. People eat stupid animals,' Fly said. 'They don't eat
clever animals. Dogs are clever animals.'

'So pigs are stupid, right, Mum?' the smallest dog asked.

Fly stopped and thought for a minute. Were pigs stupid? She
didn't know a pig, but she wanted her children to think that
she was clever and knew everything.

'Yes, they're stupid. Now, come on, let's look in the
stable.'

In one corner of the stable there was a big box for Fly and
her family. Now there was another box next to it. The young
dogs looked into the box and saw the little pig.

The pig put his head up and looked at the dogs. It wasn't
afraid, but it was very unhappy. Fly looked at the pig.

★ *sheepdog:* a farmer's dog. A sheepdog works with sheep. It moves them
round the field. A sheepdog is a very clever animal.

'Well, he's only a very small pig,' she thought. 'Maybe he's not stupid. Perhaps I made a mistake.'

Quietly, Fly said, 'Hello. Who are you?'

'I'm a Large White pig.'

The four young dogs started to laugh. 'You're a Large White pig! How big's a small white pig, then?'

'Be quiet!' their mother said. 'What's your name, little pig?'

The little pig was very sad. 'I don't know. My mother called all my brothers and sisters the same name. She called us all "Babe".'

The young dogs started to laugh again. 'Stop that noise! Go outside and play in the yard, I want to talk to this pig,' Fly said.

The dogs ran into the yard. Fly jumped into the big box next to the pig. 'Babe's a lovely name,' Fly said. 'Can I call you Babe?'

The pig started to cry. 'I want my mum,' he said very quietly.

Fly looked at the pig. 'Listen, Babe. All animals learn to leave their mothers. My young dogs are going to leave me soon. They're going to work in another village. I'm going to be sad. But you can live here with me. The boss isn't bad, we can have a good time here together.'

Babe looked at the big black and white sheepdog. 'She has four children. She's a good mother,' he thought. 'And I liked that boss man...' Suddenly Babe wasn't sad. 'Thank you, Fly,' he said. 'Perhaps I can be happy here with you.'

♦

Later that evening, Farmer Hogget and his wife came to the stables to look at the pig. Babe was in the big box next to Fly and the young dogs.

'Well, what a picture,' said Mrs Hogget. 'The pig and Fly are sleeping together. That little pig has a new mother! He doesn't know he's soon going to be on my dinner table.'

Farmer Hogget didn't look at his wife. He said nothing. Mrs Hogget left the stable and went back to her kitchen. The farmer opened the door of Fly's box and called his dog's name. Fly came and sat next to him – and the pig came too.

'Sit,' Farmer Hogget said.

Fly sat. Babe sat. Farmer Hogget looked at the two animals.

'Now what's happening here?' he asked.

Chapter 3   Learning About the Farm

Fly now had a family of five, not four. Fly showed Babe everything on the farm and he met all the animals in the yard. He did not see the sheep. They were all in the north field far away from the yard.

Then Fly remembered something. 'Babe,' she said. 'You mustn't go into Mrs Hogget's kitchen. I can go in, but you must wait outside.'

'Why can't a pig go into the kitchen?' Babe asked.

One of the young dogs said very quietly, 'You wait, little pig. One day Mrs Hogget is going to take you into the kitchen!'

'Pigs don't go there, that's all,' said Fly. But she thought, 'One day, perhaps, why not? Babe is as clever as my dogs!'

Every night Babe slept in the box with Fly and her family.

'You're a good...boy,' Fly said. She smiled. 'I nearly said a good dog!'

♦

Next morning Fly said, 'Babe, I'm going with Farmer Hogget. We're working with the sheep. You stay here with the boys.'

Fly and Farmer Hogget went to the north field.

'What's sheep?' Babe asked the young dogs.

'Well,' Babe said, 'why can't I learn to be a sheep-pig?'

'Don't you know that, you stupid little pig?' one of them answered. 'Sheep are stupid animals. They have thick coats. Dogs help the boss to work with sheep.'

'Why do you help with sheep?' Babe asked.

'Because we're sheepdogs!' they all said together. They ran out of the stable into the yard.

♦

The next week Fly's young dogs left. They went to work with sheep farmers in other villages. Fly was sad but she had Babe.

'I'm happy, Babe. I have you here,' she said. But she knew that Mrs Hogget wanted to kill Babe. She wanted to make a good Christmas dinner for Farmer Hogget.

'Mum,' Babe said, 'are your dogs going to work with sheep?'

'Yes, Babe,' Fly said. 'They're sheepdogs.'

'You're a good sheepdog, too. The boss likes you.'

'Yes, he does,' said Fly.

'Well,' Babe said, 'why can't I learn to be a sheep-pig?'

Chapter 4   Babe Meets a Sheep

One morning Fly and Babe sat in the yard with the other animals. Some ducks played in the water. Fly looked at Babe and at the ducks.

Fly said, 'Do you want a sheepdog lesson, Babe? It's very difficult to get all the ducks together. Do you want to try?'

'Oh, yes please, Mum!' Babe said.

The pig watched the ducks carefully.

'OK,' Fly said. 'You must move in behind the ducks. Sheep-dogs always run behind the sheep. The boss speaks a different language with sheepdogs. He says "Away to me" – that's right, and "Come by" is left. Do you understand? Are you ready? OK. Away to me, Babe!'

Babe started to run round the ducks. He had short legs but he ran very fast. He tried to catch the ducks, but they ran in twos and threes, here and there, all round the yard.

'Come and sit down, Babe. You're tired. Ducks are very stupid animals,' Fly said.

'But why can't I move them nicely?' Babe asked. 'They don't listen to me. Why not?'

'You're a young pig, Babe. You don't know your lessons very well. Perhaps next time . . .' Fly said.

'Can I ask them politely to listen to me, Mum?' Babe asked.

'Oh, Babe . . . ask them politely! They won't listen to you.

You must *tell* them, not *ask* them! They're stupid and sheep are stupid, too. Dogs are clever, remember.'

'But I'm a pig.'

'Yes, you are, and pigs are clever too,' Fly said.

♦

Later that morning Babe met his first sheep. Farmer Hogget put an old sheep in a big box in the stable – the sheep was ill. Babe tried to look into the box but his legs were too short.

The old sheep said, 'Wolves!' Wolves! They never stop: go here, go there, do this, do that . . . all day, every day. What do you want now?'

'I'm not a wolf,' Babe said.

'I know that,' the old sheep said. 'You're a sheepdog, I hear. You're bad, too. Go away, wolf.'

Babe climbed up and looked into the box. 'See . . . I'm not a sheepdog. I'm a pig, a Large White. My name's Babe. What's yours?'

'Maaaa,' the sheep said. 'But I'm ill. And I'm old now.'

'Well, you have a very nice name,' said Babe. 'Go to sleep now, Ma. You'll soon be better; the boss is a good man.'

Next morning Fly went to work and Babe talked to Ma.

'Good morning, Ma. Are you better today?' he asked.

'Well . . . you *are* a polite little animal. Better than a wolf. Wolves are very bad,' she said. 'Some wolves can kill sheep!'

'Oh, no! Fly isn't bad,' Babe said.

'Who's Fly?' Ma asked.

'She's my m– she's our dog here . . . works with the boss,' Babe said.

'Is that her name?' Ma asked. 'No, she's not a bad wolf. But she isn't polite. She runs round and says we're stupid. Now you're a very polite animal. You talk politely to me. You ask

*Farmer Hogget put an old sheep in the big box in the stable –
the sheep was ill. Babe tried to look into the box but his legs
were too short.*

me things. You don't think sheep are stupid. You're different,
Babe.'

Chapter 5   Bad Men at the Farm

Mrs Hogget was in the yard with Farmer Hogget.

'Look at that pig! He's running round and round the yard.
He isn't going to be fat before Christmas. And I want to kill
him for Christmas dinner. Oh well, I can wait . . . we can eat
him at Easter. What's his name?'

'Only "Pig",' answered Farmer Hogget.

He liked to see the pig in the yard with the ducks. Sometimes
the ducks walked very nicely in front of the pig, too. Farmer

Hogget did not want to kill the little pig. It was very clever.

Ma was better now. Farmer Hogget put her back in the north field with the other sheep. Babe wanted to meet the sheep.

'Sheep are interesting,' he thought. 'I want to see them and I want to see Ma again. I have a plan. Next Wednesday is market day. The boss and Mum are going to market in the next village. So I can go to see the sheep!'

◆

Babe watched everything very carefully. Fly sat in the back of the truck and Farmer Hogget drove out of the yard and down the road. He went to the market in the next village.

But other eyes watched Farmer Hogget going to market, too! Two men were behind the trees near the road. They watched the truck. Why? What did they plan to do?

Babe came out of the stable and ran up to the north field. It was a very big field. He looked round the field. Where was his new friend, Ma? Where were all the sheep?

Suddenly Babe heard a noise. He looked to his right. A lot of sheep ran up the field. Then he saw two thin black dogs behind the sheep. Babe did not know these dogs. Who were they? Why were they in Farmer Hogget's field? And why were two men there?

The sheep ran all round the field. They were very afraid.

'Wolf! Wolf!' an old sheep said. 'Danger! Danger!'

'It's you, Ma!' Babe said. 'What's happening here? Who are those men?'

'Hello, Babe,' Ma said. 'Those men are bad. Their dogs are bad, too. They know that Farmer Hogget and Fly aren't here. They want to catch us ... they want to put us in their old truck.'

'What can we do?' Babe asked.

'Do? Nothing, Babe,' Ma said. 'These dogs are very clever. Please run away, Babe.'

'I'm going to run,' said Babe, 'but I'm not going to run away! My Mum isn't here to help. But I'm not afraid. I must help you.'

Quickly Babe ran round and stood in front of the sheep. He looked at them and started to speak.

'Please, stop and listen!' he said. 'Don't be afraid! Please stop, you good, clever sheep! These dogs aren't going to catch you.'

Suddenly the sheep stopped. They all looked at Babe.

'Isn't he nice? What a polite animal!' they all said.

Then one of the dogs ran in front of Babe. The two men ran across the field and tried to hit Babe but he ran between their legs and Ma ran next to him.

'They're afraid now,' said Ma. 'They won't stay here now, with all that noise!'

In her kitchen Mrs Hogget heard all the noise and called the police. They came to catch the men, but the men drove away quickly with their dogs, but not with any sheep. Farmer Hogget's sheep quietly walked up the field together with Babe.

♦

At six o'clock Farmer Hogget came home from market. His wife told the story about the bad men.

'Oh, what a day! You left here early and these two men came. They tried to catch your sheep, up in the north field... then the police came here. Everything's OK now... You must thank him.'

'Who?' asked Farmer Hogget.

'Him!' Mrs Hogget said and she looked at Babe. 'I don't know why and I don't know how... but he's a very clever pig. He was up in the north field with the sheep. He wasn't afraid...not him! He can stay with us, in the family. I'm not going to kill him now! Oh no! Never! What do you think, my dear?'

Farmer Hogget smiled slowly.

Chapter 6 The Sheep Help Babe

The next morning Farmer Hogget wanted to take Babe and Fly to work in the north field with the sheep. He did not tell his wife.

'Come, Fly. Come, Pig,' he said.

'The boss is happy, Babe,' Fly said. 'You were a very clever pig yesterday. His sheep are OK. You can watch me work today.'

They arrived at the field and Farmer Hogget opened the big gate.

'Sit here and be quiet, Babe,' Fly said. 'I'm going to work with the sheep.'

Babe sat down quickly and watched everything. Farmer Hogget wanted the sheep to move down the field.

'Come by!' said Farmer Hogget to Fly. The sheepdog ran up the field. She ran behind the sheep.

'Go down the field!' she said to the animals. 'Down the field!'

Not one sheep moved. They looked at Fly and began to make a noise. They spoke sheep language. Fly and Farmer Hogget did not know this language, but Babe did.

The sheep were unhappy. 'Why are you not polite?' the sheep asked. 'Why don't you ask us to go down the field? We don't want you, wolf! We want Babe! We want Babe! Babe! Ba-a-a-a-be!'

Now Fly was angry. Suddenly she ran at the sheep in the front. One old sheep fell and the other sheep were afraid. They started to run all round the field.

'You aren't polite! You a-a-a-a-aren't polite!' they said. Farmer Hogget waited at the gate, but the sheep did not come down the field.

'Down, Fly,' Farmer Hogget said. 'And stay!'

He looked carefully at the animals, then he looked at Babe. The pig sat by the gate.

'I'm going to try something different,' Farmer Hogget said. 'Stay, Fly!' he said. 'Come, Pig!'

Babe looked at him. 'What does Farmer Hogget want?' he thought.

'Away to me, Pig!' Farmer Hogget said quietly.

Babe ran into the field and turned right. His little legs moved very fast. In the centre of the field he sat and waited. The sheep were very noisy. They talked loudly together. But Babe understood every word.

'Good morning, sheep,' he said. 'How are you today?'

'Hello, Babe,' one of the sheep said. 'Nice to see you again.'

'Good morning, Babe,' said another sheep. 'We're ha-a-a-appy to see you. You're a polite anima-a-a-a-a-l.'

Then Babe heard Ma. 'What's happening now? Why are you here? Where's that wolf?'

'She's not a wolf . . . remember, Ma? Fly's a sheepdog.'

'OK. She's a sheepdog. But why are you here? What do you want, Babe?' asked Ma.

'I want to be a sheep-pig,' Babe said.

'Do you now? Well, well . . . a sheep-pig,' Ma said. She looked at all the other sheep. 'Listen to me, everybody. This little pig is very good and clever. He was also very, very polite in the stable. He *asked* me to go somewhere, he didn't *tell* me.

'I want to be a sheep-pig,' Babe said.
'Do you now? Well, well . . . a sheep-pig,' Ma said.

Sheep aren't stupid and he knows that. We're clever, we are.'

'We are!' the sheep said. 'We are! We are! We a-a-a-re!'

'OK,' Ma said. 'Now what can we do for you?'

Babe looked at Farmer Hogget. He wanted the sheep to go into the sheep-pen in the corner of the field.

Babe looked at the sheep. In a quiet voice, he said, 'Good sheep, can you please walk to the gate? Farmer Hogget is waiting. Not too fast, please. Don't run . . . very slowly . . . all together, please.'

The sheep were happy to help Babe. Quietly they walked down the field to the gate and went into the sheep-pen. Nobody pushed. There was no noise.

'Good work, Babe!' Fly said. 'You did that job beautifully!'

'Thank you very much, sheep,' Babe said. 'Thank you.'

'Thank *you*, Babe,' said the sheep. 'Tha-a-a-a-nk you! You're going to be a very good sheep-pig, Ba-a-a-abe!'

Farmer Hogget was very happy.

'There's a clever pig,' he thought. 'Is he going to be a . . . ?'

'Good Pig,' he said and he closed the gate.

Chapter 7   More Lessons for Babe

Every day after that Babe went to the sheep fields with Farmer Hogget and Fly. Together they moved the sheep and put them in their sheep-pens. They worked very hard.

At night Fly and Babe talked in the stable.

'I like this work,' Babe said. 'Does the boss like me, now?'

'Yes, he does,' Fly said. 'You do the job very well, Babe. Sometimes I think the sheep know . . .'

'They do, Mum. I ask them . . .' said Babe.

'You can't *ask* sheep anything, Babe,' said Fly. 'You must *tell* them, remember?'

'Yes, Mum. But . . . can I work with the boss sometimes too? Is that OK?'

'Oh, yes, Babe, that's no problem. I ran up those fields and down those fields thousands of times. Sometimes I'm very tired. I'm not young now. I'm very happy to sit and watch you, Babe.'

So Babe started to work every day with Farmer Hogget. Fly sat and watched the pig carefully. He knew his lessons well now.

'Isn't he clever?' Farmer Hogget said. 'He can move sheep and take them to their sheep-pens. He can take a lot of sheep through the gates and he can take one sheep to the stable.'

Farmer Hogget was very happy. Babe was happy too.

15

'Mornin' Ma,' he said. 'Boss wants you to sleep in the stable.'

'Wha-a-a-at? Again?' Ma said. 'Must I go inside?'

'Yes, Ma. You're ill again. Come on now, please,' Babe said.

'OK Pig. You a-a-a-a-are so polite. I like you,' said Ma.

Farmer Hogget started to make a plan. 'I want to take Babe to the sheepdog trials,' he thought. 'Sheepdogs work at trials. People from the town and other farmers come to watch them. Babe can sit and watch too. But I'm not going to tell my wife.'

Next day Fly worked the sheep and Babe watched. The sheep were afraid.

'Wolf! Wolf!' they said and they ran round and round the field.

'Quickly! Go! Go into your sheep-pens,' Fly said. She was never polite to them.

'We want Babe!' the sheep said. 'We want Ba-a-a-a-abe!'

They ran into the sheep-pens but they were not happy.

'Easy, Fly,' said Farmer Hogget. 'Easy, old girl!'

He never said 'Easy' to Babe.

◆

It was a sunny morning. Farmer Hogget put Fly and Babe into the back of the big truck.

He drove ten miles to another village. Many farmers from other villages were there with their sheepdogs.

'I want to watch the other sheepdogs but nobody is going to see my... my sheep-pig!' he said. The truck stopped at the end of the road. 'This is a very good place to leave the truck. Now nobody knows we're here. Come, Fly! Come, Pig!'

Farmer Hogget walked quickly.

'Where are we going, Mum?' Babe asked. 'What are we going to do this morning?'

*It was a sunny morning. Farmer Hogget put Fly and Babe
into the back of the big truck.*

'I don't know,' answered Fly. 'Perhaps the boss wants you
to see something.'

They were near some large trees. Farmer Hogget stopped.

'Down, Fly. Down Pig, and stay!' the farmer said and he sat
down beside Fly under the trees.

'Wants me to see what?' Babe asked.

'The trials,' said Fly. 'They're for sheepdogs and their bosses.
Each dog tries to move the sheep quickly from one place to
another. Every trial is different. Today the sheep must go down
the field into a big sheep-pen. Then the dog must take only

three sheep and put them into another sheep-pen. Then the dog must put all the sheep back together again in the big sheep-pen.'

'Is that all, Mum?' Babe asked.

'Yes, but it isn't easy. You must run quickly. You can't make a mistake. It's difficult work, Babe. Watch and you'll see.'

Babe looked at the dogs. Yes, it was very difficult work. The sheep ran very fast and the dogs made some mistakes at the gate.

Babe watched everything. Farmer Hogget watched Babe and Fly watched her boss and her clever Babe.

The trials finished in the afternoon and Farmer Hogget drove his two animals home in the truck.

'What's the boss going to do?' Fly said. 'Does he think Babe is as clever as . . . no! All the other farmers will laugh . . . he's clever but not a . . . sheep-pig!'

Then she remembered something. She looked at Babe.

'Weren't the dogs at the trials clever, Babe?' she asked.

'Oh, yes, Mum,' Babe said. 'They were very clever. But here's the problem . . . they weren't polite!'

Chapter 8   Babe Helps the Sheep

Farmer Hogget thought about his plan every day. He put two gates in the centre of the field. Babe asked the sheep very politely to go through the new gates. The farmer made a new small road in the field. Babe asked the sheep to go very quietly down the new road. The sheep were happy to work with Babe.

Then Farmer Hogget made two new sheep-pens in two different corners of the field. The gates for the sheep-pens were very small. Every day Fly took five sheep to the north corner of the field and waited there with them.

Then it was Babe's job to move the sheep.

'Away to me, Pig!' the farmer said, or 'Come by, Pig!' and Babe ran fast to the corner of the field. Farmer Hogget always looked at his watch. There was one problem. Babe must run faster.

Fly watched everything carefully.

'Yes,' she said, 'Babe is clever. The sheep always go with him. But he knows all the sheep here. At the trials it's going to be different sheep. What's going to happen then? Can he work with them?'

That night she ate her dinner in the stable with Babe. She looked at him carefully.

'He's a big boy. He likes his food, but he eats too much!' she thought. 'He eats a very big dinner every night. Now he's too fat.'

Babe finished his dinner and sat down. He was happy.

'Babe, do you like this . . . sheep-pig's job?' Fly asked.

'Oh, yes, Mum!' Babe said.

'Do you want to be a better sheep-pig?' Fly asked. 'Perhaps the best?'

'Yes, I do, Mum. But how can I? Dogs run faster than pigs. That's a big problem.'

'I can help you. You can do two things. You must run more every day. And run fast . . . up the field, down the field, round the yard again and again.'

'OK Mum,' Babe said. 'What's the other thing?'

'Don't eat so much food. You're too fat, Babe,' Fly said.

'OK. I can do that,' Babe said. 'I can eat a smaller dinner.'

Babe started to run round the yard every morning. In the afternoon he ran up and down the fields. Every day he ran. He ran faster and faster. Every night he ate a smaller dinner.

A week later, Farmer Hogget looked at the pig.

'Well, well, that pig's not too fat now. He's bigger, too, and stronger. And he runs faster. What a good sheep-pig!'

♦

One beautiful morning Fly said, 'Are you ready, Babe? It's time to run. Go to the south field this morning. I'll wait here.'

Babe left and Fly went to sleep.

♦

Babe went into the yard. He was very happy. He wanted to see Ma and the other sheep. He wanted to say 'Good morning, everybody! Isn't it a lovely day?' He ran to the south field.

Where were the sheep? He looked round the field. Then he heard a sound in the corner of the field.

'Wolf! Wolf! Help! Help!'

'What's happening?' Babe said and he turned to look.

There were two large bad dogs in the field! Babe remembered Ma's words, 'Some wolves can kill sheep!'

He ran down the field. He was not afraid.

♦

The noise was worse now. The sheep were in every corner of the field. They were very afraid. Some sheep tried to jump over the gate but they fell.

One young sheep said, 'Help me! Help me!'

One sheep was in the centre of the field. The dogs moved in and the sheep said, 'Wolf! Wolf! It's going to kill me!'

Now Babe was very angry. 'That dog's going to kill the sheep,' he thought. 'I must do something!'

Babe ran at the smaller, brown dog. His teeth went into the dog's back and he threw the dog away from the sheep. The dog ran quickly to the gate. It was very afraid now.

20

Babe was very happy. He want to see Ma and the other sheep.
He wanted to say 'Good morning, everybody! Isn't it a
lovely day?'

Then the other dog came nearer to Babe. It was bigger and stronger than the small dog. It wasn't afraid!

Again Babe showed his teeth – this time to the big dog. The big dog started to fight. Babe put his teeth into the big dog's back legs. The big dog pushed Babe hard but Babe wasn't afraid! He was angrier now. Then Babe put his big teeth in the dog's back and threw the dog into the corner of the field. The dog tried to fight again, but Babe was too strong. The two dogs ran out of the field.

Babe ran to look at the sheep. They were all in the centre of the field together. One sheep was very ill. It was Ma!

'Ma! Ma!' Babe said. 'Are you OK?'

'Is that you, Babe?' answered the old sheep. She tried to turn her head to Babe. 'I can't see you.'

'It's OK now, Ma. The dogs ran away,' Babe said.

'Far, far, fa-a-a-ar away,' all the sheep said together.

'It's going to be OK, Ma,' Babe said. 'The boss is coming.'

Ma said nothing. She closed her eyes. Everything was quiet. The sheep looked sad. There was no noise in the field.

'Oh, Ma!' Babe cried.

'Ma! Ma! Ma-a-a-a-a-a-a!' all the sheep cried together.

♦

Farmer Hogget and Fly came into the field.

'Where are all the sheep? What's happening?' asked Farmer Hogget. 'Come by, Fly!'

Then he saw the sheep. He saw old Ma.

'Who killed this sheep?' asked Farmer Hogget.

He looked at Babe. His face was very angry.

Chapter 9   Babe in Danger

'Go home, Pig!' Farmer Hogget said. 'Go home!'

Babe did not understand. 'Why is he angry? Why must I go home? I want to stay here with Fly,' thought Babe.

But he was a good pig and he went home. The farmer put Ma in his truck. Then Fly moved the sheep and put them in the sheep-pens. They went very quietly this time.

'Stay, Fly!' Farmer Hogget. 'I'm going to the farmhouse.'

♦

Babe was in the stable. He felt very, very sad. It was not a good day now. In the morning he was happy but he felt very different now.

'Why is the boss so angry? I helped the sheep...' thought Babe.

He sat at the door of the stable. He saw the truck. It came into the yard. He saw the boss. Farmer Hogget went into the house and came out again. What was that long, black thing in his hand?

'Come, Pig!' he said. His voice was angry and hard. At that minute Mrs Hogget heard the phone in the kitchen.

Babe followed the farmer into the stable. He sat down and waited. 'Is that long, black thing for me? Does it make food or something? The boss is putting it very near my mouth.'

'Hogget! Where are you?' Mrs Hogget said. She looked out of her kitchen window. 'There's bad news. Where are you?'

'Here, wife... in the stable,' Farmer Hogget said. He put the long, black thing in the box next to Babe. 'What's happening?'

Mrs Hogget ran to the stable door.

'Oh! There you are,' she said. 'That was the police on the

23

phone. They're telling all the farmers the same news. There are two bad dogs near here. They killed six sheep in the next village last night. One big black dog and a smaller brown one. You must try to kill them! Go and see our sheep! Go quickly! Are our sheep OK?'

'Yes,' answered Farmer Hogget. 'Our sheep are OK.'

Mrs Hogget went to the kitchen and Farmer Hogget walked into the yard. Babe followed him.

'Sit, Pig,' he said quietly. His voice was not hard now. He looked carefully at Babe's face. He saw some brown hairs and some black hairs near the pig's mouth.

'Well, well,' he said. '*You* weren't afraid. Aren't you a clever little pig?'

Fly waited in the field. She was not happy.

'Who killed that old sheep?' she said. 'Some dogs can kill sheep . . . but a sheep–pig cannot kill a sheep! I must know!'

Fly went to ask the sheep in the pens.

'Who killed that old sheep?' she asked. 'Was it the pig? Was it Babe? Tell me, you stupid animals!'

'Wolf! Wolf!' one sheep said.

'Was it or wasn't it Babe, you stupid things?' asked Fly.

'Ba-a-a-a-abe!' another sheep said.

'I must know,' Fly thought. 'Can I *ask* them? Babe is always polite . . . he asks them.' She looked at the sheep. 'Please . . .' she said. 'Good, clever sheep . . . please tell me.'

The sheep looked at Fly. '*The wolf is asking us!*' they said.

'Babe! Ba-a-a-abe came! The wolves ran awa-a-a-ay! Babe came! The wolves ran awa-a-a-ay!' they all said together.

Babe was not a bad sheep–pig. He was the best!

'Thank you, good, clever sheep. Thank you!' Fly said.

Farmer Hogget and the pig came into the sheep pen.

'Well, now,' Babe said to Fly. 'Aren't you polite?'

Chapter 10 The Password

Farmer Hogget and his wife were very happy. The farmer gave Babe a lot of food, but Babe ate only his small dinner. So Fly ate Babe's food and she got fatter and fatter.

Babe now went into the kitchen with the dog and Mrs Hogget. One day Farmer Hogget came into the kitchen for his dinner. Fly and Babe were there. They sat next to him and they watched the news on television together.

'That pig likes television,' said Mrs Hogget. 'Isn't he a good little pig? But he's not little, now... he's big and strong. He's more clever than a dog, too. Perhaps he can learn to work with sheep! What do you think, Farmer Hogget?'

Farmer Hogget smiled. 'I'm not telling her about my plan,' he thought. 'I'm going to take Babe to the British Sheepdog Trials. I never tried with my sheepdogs, but now I have Babe. We're going to try to be the best! Perhaps we'll be on television!'

The plan was easy. 'I'm going to take Fly with me. The farmers will see me with a sheepdog at the trials. But at the last minute I'm going to put Babe in the field with the sheep.'

He read the paper about the trials. It said: British Sheepdog Trials. Name of Farmer and Name of Animal.

'That's good,' Farmer Hogget said. 'It says "Animal", not "Dog", so I can write "Pig".'

♦

Farmer Hogget and Babe started to work very hard.

'We must be ready next week,' Farmer Hogget said. 'Babe is going to work with the sheep every morning and every afternoon.'

25

Babe brought the sheep up the field, through the gates and into the sheep-pens. He moved five sheep into the big sheep-pen and two sheep into the small sheep-pen. He did very well.

Every night after dinner Babe and Fly talked in the stable.

'Mum,' said Babe. '*I* am going to try to be the best at the sheepdog trials. You're a clever sheepdog, too, but Farmer Hogget only put my name on the papers. Is that a problem?'

'No, Babe,' answered Fly. 'It's not a problem. I'm older now and fatter! I want you to be the best. And you *can* be the best, Babe!'

But Fly knew some things. The sheepdogs ran faster than Babe. Farmer Hogget's sheep knew Babe. He asked them politely to go into the sheep-pens.

'The sheep at the trials will be different,' Fly thought. 'Can Babe talk to them? How can he move them into the sheep-pens quickly? I must ask our sheep.'

The next evening Fly went to the field. The sheep all listened very carefully.

'Good evening, good, clever sheep,' Fly started. 'Can you help me, please? Babe is going to the British Sheepdog Trials with Farmer Hogget. They want to be the best. But there's a problem.'

She told them the problem. 'They'll be different sheep at the trials . . . what can he say to them? He can ask them politely, but they never saw a sheep-pig before . . . so what can he do?'

'Password,' one of the sheep said.

'Password, pa-a-a-a-assword,' all the sheep said together. 'Babe must learn the password.'

'What's that?' asked Fly.

'All sheep know the pa-a-a-assword. Young sheep learn it from their mothers. Mother sheep say the password and little sheep don't run away!'

'Please, what is the password?' asked Fly. 'Please tell me, good, clever sheep...it's for Babe.'

The sheep were quiet.

'It's for Babe,' one little sheep said. 'For good Ba-a-a-abe.'

They all spoke together

> *'We can be he, we can be she,*
> *But we're all sheep, you can see.*
> *We cannot read or write a book*
> *But we're not as stupid as we look.'*

Fly asked, 'Is that the password?'

'A-a-a-a-a-a-a-a-r,' said the sheep.

In the stable that night Fly told Babe the password.

'I don't understand it, Mum,' the pig said.

'Learn it by heart, Babe,' Fly said. 'Don't you want to be the best?'

'It's for Babe,' one little sheep said. 'For good Ba-a-a-abe.'

Chapter 11   The Sheepdog Trials

It was early morning. Farmer Hogget stood in the yard and looked at the sky.

'It's going to rain today,' he said. He went into the farmhouse and got his raincoat.

In the stable Fly looked at Babe. 'Today's the day, Babe! The day of the British Sheepdog Trials. And you, Babe, are going to be the best!'

She looked at the pig carefully.

'But you're so dirty! Playing with those ducks again?' she asked. 'I know you are a Large White, but nobody can see your colour. What can we do?'

At that minute Farmer Hogget came into the stable.

'Come, Pig,' he said. 'Time to wash you. Let's go!'

He washed Babe carefully in warm water, from his head to his short legs. Half an hour later, Babe was nice and clean.

Mrs Hogget opened the kitchen window. 'Breakfast's ready!' she said. 'What are you doing? Why are you washing the pig? Aren't you going up to the trials today? Is the pig going with you? People are going to laugh at you with a pig in the truck. What's he going to do at a sheepdog trial? Is he going to sit and watch?'

'No,' Farmer Hogget answered.

'Well then, what? He isn't going to . . .' she said. She looked at Farmer Hogget and she looked at Babe. Then without another word she closed the window.

♦

After breakfast Farmer Hogget was ready to leave. Fly sat in the front of the truck and Babe sat in the back.

Mrs Hogget looked at the two animals.

'Good boy,' she said to Babe and 'Good girl,' to Fly. To Farmer Hogget she said, 'Goodbye...take this food with you ...and your raincoat. It's going to rain later. Do you know the road? Please drive carefully...not too fast with these animals. See you later!'

'Two o'clock,' Farmer Hogget said. 'On television.'

He drove out of the farmyard.

♦

At two o'clock Mrs Hogget sat down to watch television. It was raining at the trials. A man spoke to the farmers.

'The trials start here. The farmer stands at the gate and the dogs start from here, too. The animal can run left or right to move the sheep. Each dog has ten sheep to work with. The sheep must come through the Village Gate and round it. Then the sheep must go through the Away Gates, turn right, and go through the Green Gates. Then turn left to the Village Sheep-Pen. Five sheep must stay in the Village Sheep-Pen and the other five go to the small Catch Sheep-Pen by the gate.'

'Talk, talk, talk,' Mrs Hogget said. 'All those gates and everything. Why can't we see the farmers and their dogs? I want to see Fly and Farmer Hogget...not Babe. He'll stay in the truck. Why isn't Babe here with me to watch these trials on the television? That pig likes television. Too much talk, talk, talk. I don't like too much talk. I'm going to work in the kitchen.'

She left the room. On the television the first farmer and his dog started work.

Chapter 12   The Best in the World

Hogget, Fly and Babe watched the first dog carefully. The truck was under some large trees in the corner of the car park. Nobody saw the farmer and his animals.

'It's very windy,' Farmer Hogget thought. 'It's very difficult for the sheepdogs today.'

The first dog got seventy points out of a hundred.

All the dogs tried to get one hundred points. Dogs from Scotland, England, Ireland and Wales all tried to move the sheep quickly. There were big dogs, little dogs, black dogs and brown dogs. Some dogs got more points than other dogs. The best dog got eighty-five points.

Mrs Hogget was in front of the television again. She listened carefully.

'One more to go,' said the man on the television. 'The best dog has eighty-five points. That's very good. The dogs have a very difficult job today. But we have one more farmer . . .'

And there was Farmer Hogget on television!

'Well, well, look at him! And look at our dog, Fly!' she said.

The man spoke again. 'This is farmer Hogget with Pig. What a name for a dog! . . . And the dog's too fat . . . wait a minute, the dog is going . . . What's that? . . . Can you see that?'

Mrs Hogget and thousands of other people looked at the field. Fly went to the car park and a Large White pig ran into the field in her place!

Babe stood next to Farmer Hogget and waited. There was a lot of noise from the other farmers. Some people started to laugh. Babe and Farmer Hogget waited quietly.

The man spoke again. 'Well, the papers for the trials said

Babe stood next to Farmer Hogget and waited.

"Animal" not "Dog", so Farmer Hogget can work with a ... sheep-pig! Ha, ha! We'll finish the trials today with a good laugh.'

Everybody laughed at Farmer Hogget and Babe as they went to the middle of the field.

'Away to me, Pig,' Farmer Hogget said quietly.

Babe started to run left, behind the sheep. He ran fast. Some people laughed, but other farmers watched the pig carefully. His little legs went faster and faster.

Babe ran to the sheep. He spoke the password in a loud voice. '*We can be she, we can be he, But we're all sheep, you can see. We cannot read or write a book, but we're not as stupid as we look.*'

The rain fell and it was very windy. He saw the ten sheep at the gate. Twenty eyes looked at Babe. They listened to him.

Babe spoke again, '... *but we're not as stupid as we look.* Good afternoon, good, clever sheep. How are you today? It isn't nice to work in the rain, but ...'

Babe heard the noise of excited sheep voices.

'How can he know the pa-a-a-assword? What a polite pig!'

'Not the same as the ba-a-a-ad wolves!' they said.

'What do you wa-a-a-ant? How can we help you, young ma-a-an?'

Quickly, Babe told them.

'And can you move all together, please? Not too fast, not too slow. Walk through the Village Gates over there. Then turn to the right, go through the Away Gates and the Green Gates. Then please turn left into the Village Sheep-Pen. Then the five biggest can go into the Catch Sheep-Pen by the gate.'

People waited. Mrs Hogget watched at home.

'What's the pig going to do?' everybody said.

Suddenly, the sheep began to walk through the Village Gates,

'And can you move all together, please? Not too fast,
not too slow.'

with Babe behind them. They walked together, heads up, in
twos. Twenty points!

They turned right. They looked at Babe and they went
quietly through the Away Gates. Well done! Forty points!

Nobody laughed now. The ten sheep walked two by two
through the Green Gates. Well done! Sixty points!

Now a more difficult job. The sheep turned right and walked
into the big Village Sheep-Pen. Eighty points!

Nobody laughed now. Everybody spoke at the same time.

'Isn't he good?'

'What lovely work!'

'But can he put five sheep into the Catch Sheep-Pen? Can he do better than that dog with eighty-five points?'

Babe waited outside the Village Sheep-Pen. Farmer Hogget looked at his watch. Babe watched Farmer Hogget very carefully.

Mrs Hogget waited.

Everybody at the trials waited.

Babe walked to his sheep and quietly said, 'You did a good job. Thank you very much, you clever sheep. Now I want the five biggest sheep. Please go into the Catch Sheep-Pen by the gate. The other five wait here. Thank you very much. Can you do that now, please?'

'A-a-a-a-a-r,' they said, and the five big sheep went into the Catch Sheep-Pen.

Farmer Hogget walked into the field. He closed the gate of the Catch Sheep-Pen. One hundred points! One hundred points for Babe.

Everybody started to make a noise. Mrs Hogget was very happy.

'Babe did it! He did it!' she said. 'One hundred points!'

From the truck Fly saw Farmer Hogget and Babe.

'He did it! Babe got one hundred points!' she said. 'He's the best in the world!'

Farmer Hogget and Babe stood together. The rain stopped. The wind stopped. It was sunny now.

Nobody heard Farmer Hogget's words to his sheep-pig.

'Well done, Pig!' he said. 'You're the best.'

One hundred points! One hundred points for Babe.

ACTIVITIES

Chapters 1–2

Before you read

1 Look at the Word List at the back of the book and find any new
   words in your dictionary. Then answer the questions.
   a Which of these is not an animal?
      duck   pig   yard   wolf
   b Which of these can you drive?
      farm   gate   truck   yard
   c Which of these do horses live in?
      market   stable   trial   truck
   d Which of these isn't on a farm?
      field   sheep-pen   yard   gate   market
2 Read the Introduction to this book and answer these questions.
   a Does the story happen in a village or in a city?
   b Is a sheep-pig a sheep or a pig?
   c Is Fly a sheep, a pig or a dog?
   d Which were Dick King Smith's jobs before he was a writer?
3 Fly says in the story, 'People eat stupid animals. They don't eat
   clever animals. Dogs are clever animals.' Which animals do you
   think are stupid? Which are clever?

While you read

4 Put these words in the right places.
      box   dinners   doesn't want   Fly
      happy   Large White   ticket   wants   wins
   a The .... for the pig costs 10 pence.
   b Mrs Hogget can make two .... from a fat pig.
   c Farmer Hogget .... the pig.
   d Fly and her young dogs find a pig in a ....
   e The little pig isn't ....

36

   f The little pig is a .... pig.

   g .... is kind to Babe.

   h Mrs Hogget .... to eat Babe.

   i Farmer Hogget .... to eat Babe.

After you read

  5 Have this conversation with a student. You are at the village party.
'Win a Pig!' calls the man with Babe. 'How heavy is he?'

     Student A: You are selling tickets.

     Student B: You want to buy a ticket.

Chapters 3–5

Before you read

  6 Answer these questions. What do you think?

   a Why must Fly's young dogs leave the farm?

   b How can Babe show Mrs Hogget that he is clever?

While you read

  7 Answer *Yes* or *No* to these questions.

   a Can Fly's young dogs go into the kitchen?   .....

   b Do any of the young dogs stay on the Hogget farm?   .....

   c Does Babe know that he will be Christmas dinner?   .....

   d Do the ducks follow Babe?   .....

   e Does Ma like Babe?   .....

   f Can dogs kill sheep sometimes?   .....

  8 Who does these things? Finish the sentences.

   a .... and .... go to market on Wednesdays.

   b .... watch when Farmer Hogget drives away.

   c .... cries 'Wolf!' when she sees the two dogs.

   d The .... try to hit Babe.

   e .... telephones the police.

   f .... doesn't want to kill Babe now.

9 What do these words mean? Who says them?

    a 'Away to me.'   **b** 'Come by.'   **c** 'Wolf!'

10 Which animals are on the Hogget farm? Tick (✓) them.

    dog .....   cat .....   sheep .....   pig .....

    wolf .....   chickens .....   ducks .....   horse .....

Chapters 6–7

Before you read

11 In the next chapter Farmer Hogget says, 'Stay, Fly!' and 'Come, Pig!' What do you think this means for Fly and Babe?

While you read

12 <u>Underline</u> the mistake in each sentence. Write the right word.

    a Farmer Hogget takes his wife and Babe to the

       north field.   ....

    b Babe can't speak sheep language.   ....

    c Babe has very long legs and can run fast.   ....

    d The sheep think that Fly is very polite.   ....

    e Babe knows that sheep are stupid.   ....

    f Fly is angry because Babe does the job well. ....

13 What do the dogs do at the trials? Write in these words.

    back   down   in   into   through

    a They take the sheep .... the field into the big pen.

    b They must take three sheep .... the gate and ....

       a small pen.

    c They take the three sheep .... to the big pen.

    d They must finish .... three minutes.

After you read

14 Discuss these questions.

    a Why does Farmer Hogget take Babe to the sheep trials?

    b Are there animal trials in your country? What animals do they use? What do they do?

Chapters 8–9

Before you read

15 Discuss these questions.

    a Babe is a good sheep-pig but what are his two problems?

    b Somebody nearly kills Babe in Chapter 9. What do you think will happen?

While you read

16 Are these sentences right (✓) or wrong (✗)?

    a Pigs can't run as fast as dogs. .....

    b Pigs like eating. .....

    c Sheep aren't afraid of dogs. .....

    d Dogs can't kill sheep. .....

    o Old Ma is dead. .....

    f Farmer Hogget thinks that Fly killed Ma. .....

    g He goes to the stable with his gun. .....

    h Mrs Hogget phones the police. .....

    i Farmer Hogget finds dog hairs on Babe's mouth. .....

    j Fly learns to talk to the sheep. .....

After you read

17 Work with another student. Have this conversation.

The police telephone Mrs Hogget about the two dogs.

Student A: You are the policeman/woman.

Student B: You are Mrs Hogget.

Chapters 10–11

Before you read

18 The next chapter is 'The Password'. Who do you think will want a password? What for?

19 Finish the sentences on the left with words on the right.

  a Fly and Babe like .....   **f** before the Trials.

  b Farmer Hogget never took ..... **g** watching television.

  c Babe works hard .....   **h** Fly to the Sheepdog Trials.

  d Fly teaches Babe .....   **i** the morning of the Trials.

  e Babe has a bath on .....   **j** the password.

After you read

20 These sentences are in the wrong places. What happens first? What happens next?

  a Leave five sheep there.   .....

  b Start at the gate.   .....

  c Take five sheep to the Catch-Pen.   .....

  d Take ten sheep through the Away Gates and turn right.   .....

  e Take ten sheep through the Green Gates. .....

  f Take ten sheep through the Village Gate. .....

  g Turn left to the Village Sheep-Pen.   .....

Chapter 12

Before you read

21 Which of these will happen, do you think?

  a They will stop Babe because he is a pig.

  b They will laugh when they see Babe.

  c Babe will be the best in the world.

While you read

22 Write in the number of points.

  The first dog gets ..... points.

  The best dog gets ..... points.

  Babe gets ..... points.

After you read

23 Answer the questions.

    a Is it nice weather when Babe starts the Trials?

    b Why do the sheep help Babe?

    c Is it nice weather when Babe finishes the Trials?

Writing

24 The police want the two men with the two thin dogs in Chapter 5. They put up a paper in the village shop. At the top it says, 'We want these men!' Write the other words.

25 You are giving points at the Sheep Dog Trials. You watch Babe at the end. Write your notes.

26 You work for a newspaper. You are at the Sheep Dog Trials. You watch Babe. Talk to all the other farmers. What do they think of Babe? Write a story for your newspaper.

27 It is the day after the Trials. Write one of these conversations:

    a Farmer Hogget and Mrs Hogget in the kitchen.

    b Babe and Fly in the stable.

28 Pigs and dogs are clever. What other animals are clever? Find out about one and write about it.

29 Farmer Hogget wins Babe at the village party. You are having a village party. You want people to come. There will be games, food, drink, animals. Write a note for the village shop window.

30 Write about one of the photographs from the film. What is happening? What happened before? What is going to happen?

31 Do animals talk? Write one of these conversations:

    a A horse and a sheep in a field.

    b A dog and a cat in front of the kitchen fire.

Answers for the Activities in this book are available from the Penguin Readers website. A free Activity Worksheet is also available from the website. Activity Worksheets are part of the Penguin Teacher Support Programme, which also includes Progress Tests and Graded Reader Guidelines. For more information, please visit: www.penguinreaders.com.

WORD LIST *with example sentences*

corner (n) A square has four *corners*.

duck (n) The *ducks* on the water flew away.

farm (n) My uncle is a farmer. He has a big *farm* with a lot of animals.

field (n) There are three horses in that *field*.

gate (n) Remember to shut the garden *gate*.

market (n) You can buy vegetables at the Wednesday *market*.

must (v) We haven't got any food. We *must* buy some.

password (n) We can't go in because we don't know the *password*.

pig (n) *Pigs* are quite big animals, but they have short legs.

point (n) We won the game by 6 *points*.

polite (adj) He is always friendly and *polite*.

sheep (n) *Sheep* are animals with thick warm coats.

sheepdog (n) The man and his *sheepdog* moved the sheep to the next field.

sheep-pen (n) They are trying to get all the sheep into a *sheep-pen*.

stable (n) We bring the horses into the *stable* at night.

together (adv) Let's work *together*. I can help you, and you can help me.

trial (n) He did very well in the sheepdog *trials*. His dog was the best.

truck (n) We put the animals in the back of the *truck* and drove them home.

wolf (n) Is that animal a *wolf* or a big dog?

yard (n) There were some chickens and a car in the *yard* in front of the farmhouse.

Fly Away Home
Patricia Hermes

Amy Alden finds a nest of goose eggs, but there isn't a mother goose. So she takes the eggs home. The baby geese think Amy is their mother. They follow her everywhere. But when the winter comes, they must fly south. Can Amy help them to fly away?

The Jungle Book
Rudyard Kipling

A family of wolves takes a little boy into their home in the jungle. The child learns and plays with the other cubs. But can he really live in the jungle? Will the other wolves want him to stay? And will the dangerous tiger Shere Khan catch him?

Black Beauty
Anna Sewell

'Always be good, so people will love you. Always work hard and do your best.'

These were the words of Black Beauty's mother to her son when they lived with Farmer Grey. But when Black Beauty grew up and his life changed, this was sometimes very difficult for him. Not everybody was as kind as Farmer Grey.

Longman Dictionaries

Express yourself with confidence!

*Longman has led the way in ELT dictionaries since 1935.
We constantly talk to students and teachers around the
world to find out what they need from a learner's dictionary.*

Why choose a Longman dictionary?

Easy to understand

Longman invented the Defining Vocabulary – 2000 of the most common words which are used to write the definitions in our dictionaries. So Longman definitions are always clear and easy to understand.

Real, natural English

All Longman dictionaries contain natural examples taken from real-life that help explain the meaning of a word and show you how to use it in context.

Avoid common mistakes

Longman dictionaries are written specially for learners, and we make sure that you get all the help you need to avoid common mistakes. We analyse typical learners' mistakes and include notes on how to avoid them.

Innovative CD-ROMs

Longman are leaders in dictionary CD-ROM innovation. Did you know that a dictionary CD-ROM includes features to help improve your pronunciation, help you practice for exams and improve your writing skills?

**For details of all Longman dictionaries, and to choose
the one that's right for you, visit our website:**

www.longman.com/dictionaries